A Ride

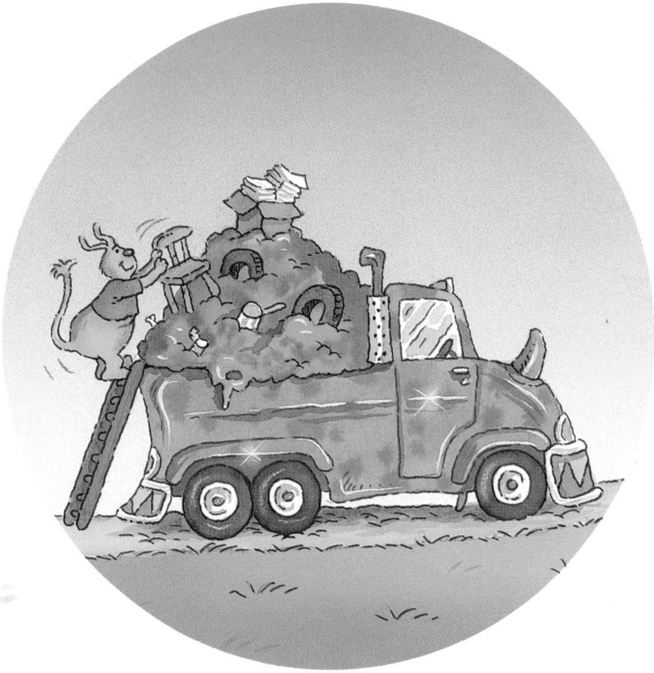

Illustrated by Richard Hoit

PEARSON

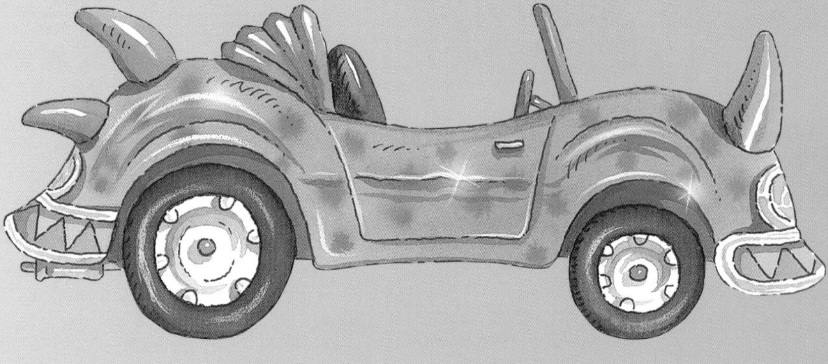

A car.

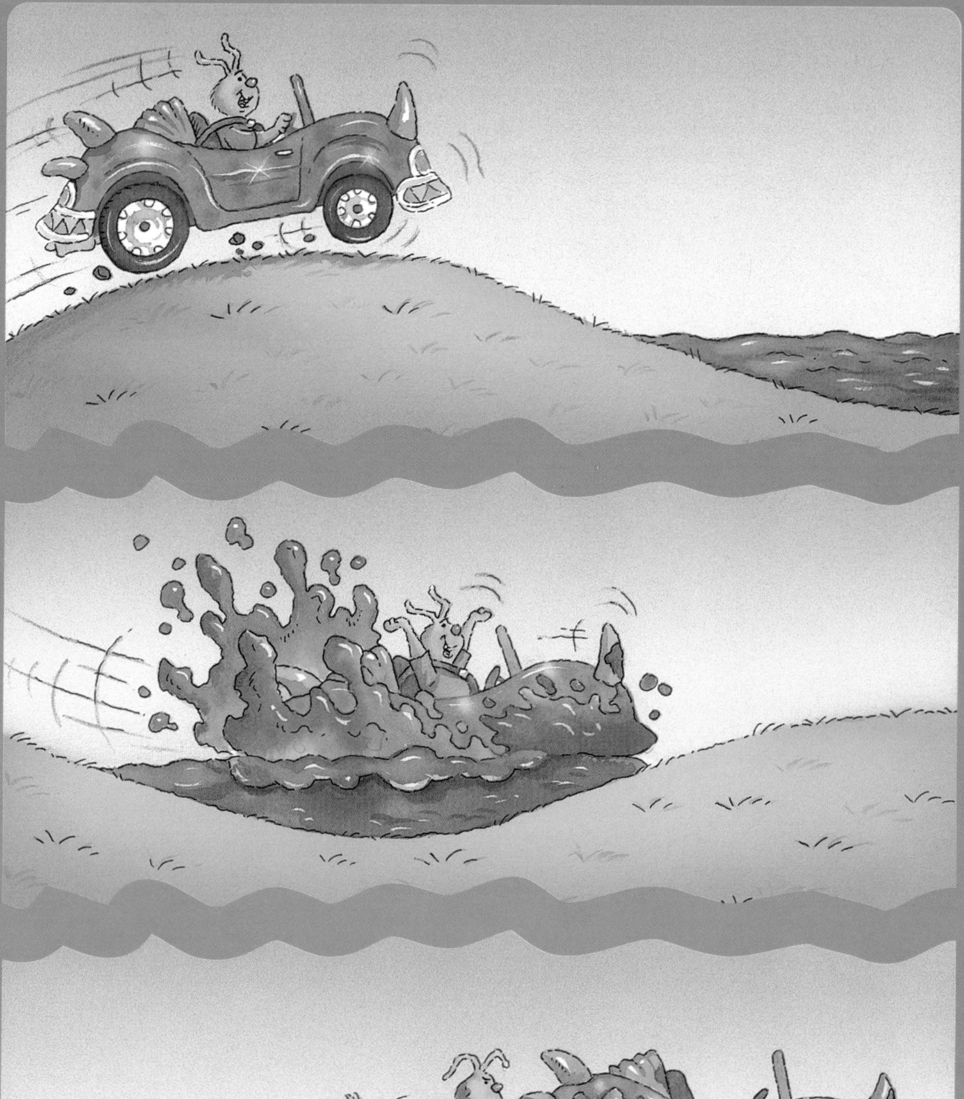

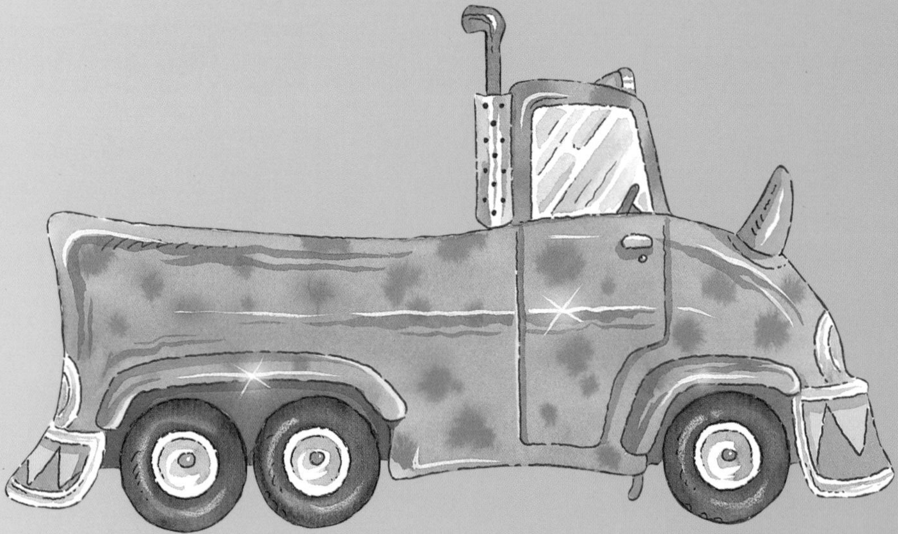

A truck.

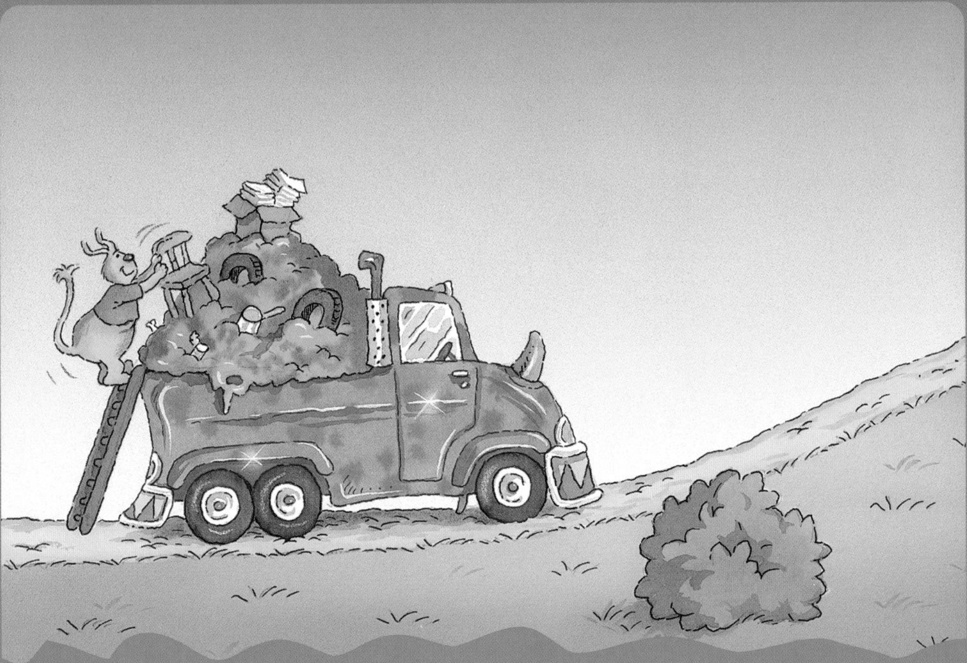

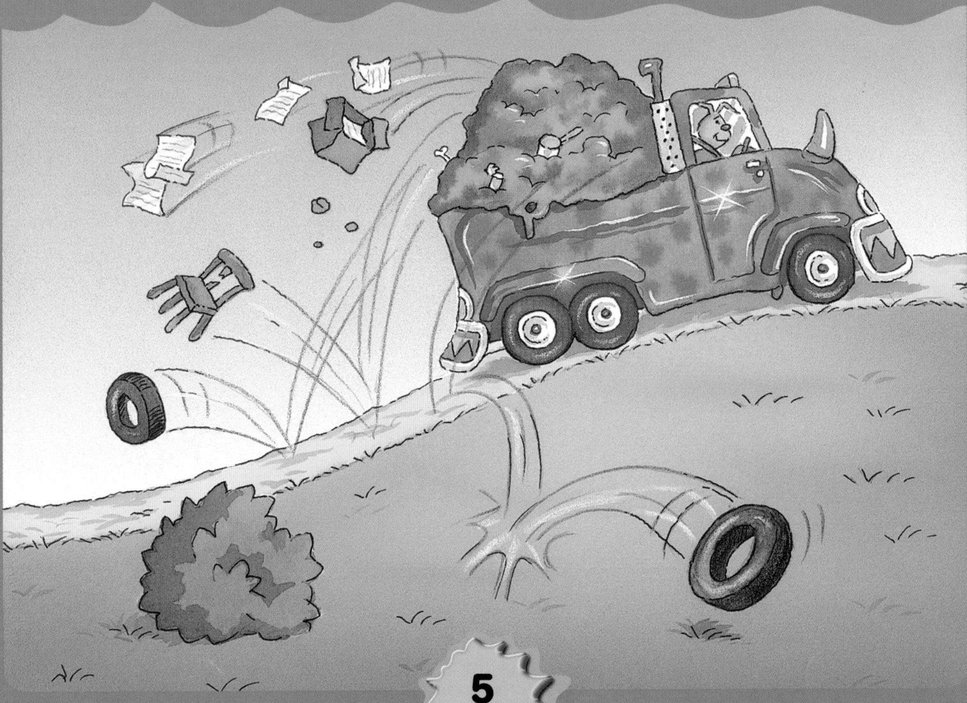

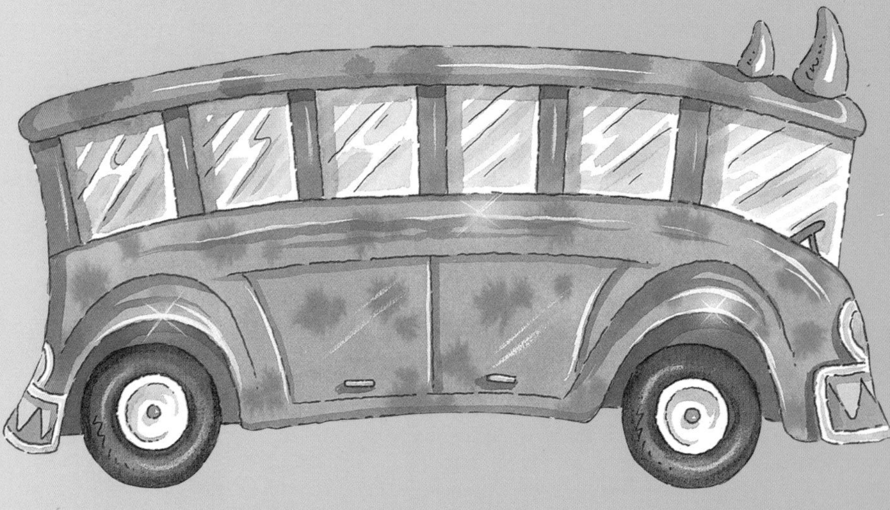

A bus.

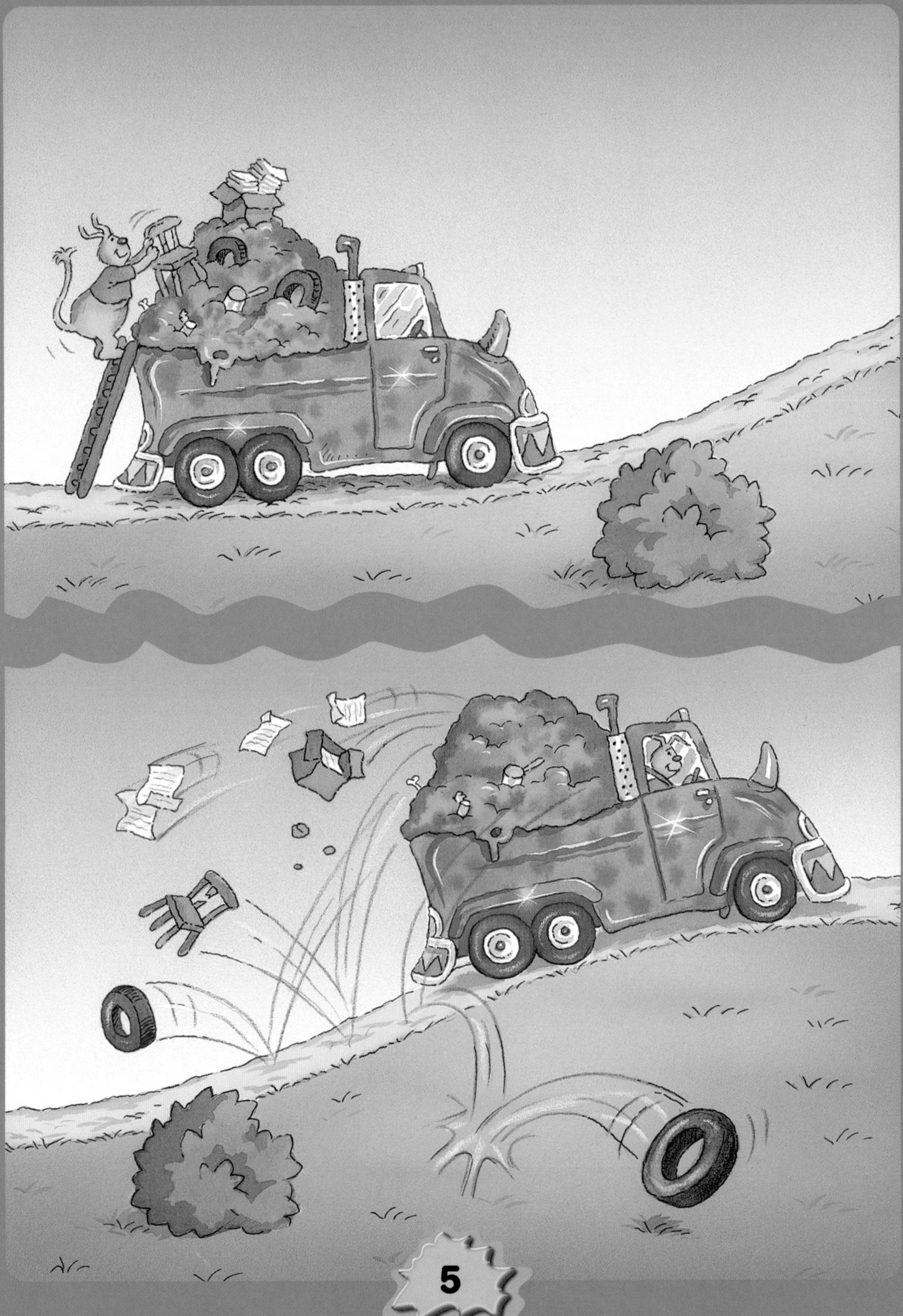

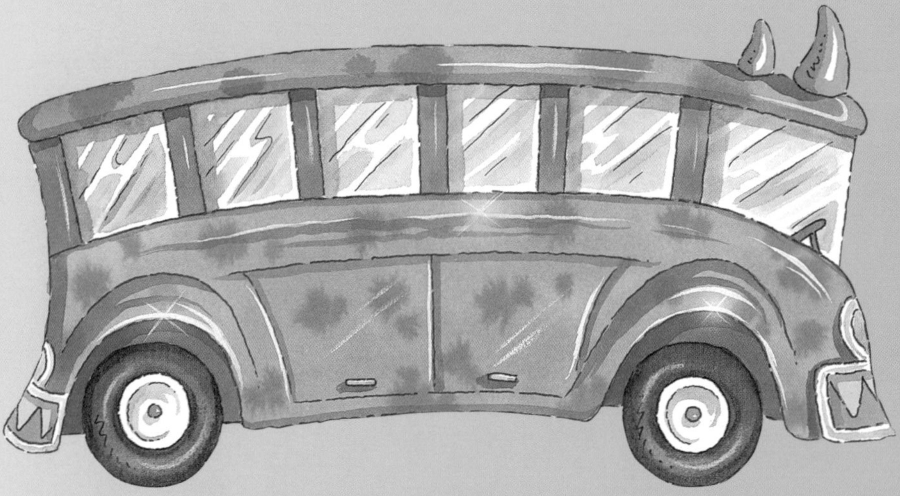

A bus.

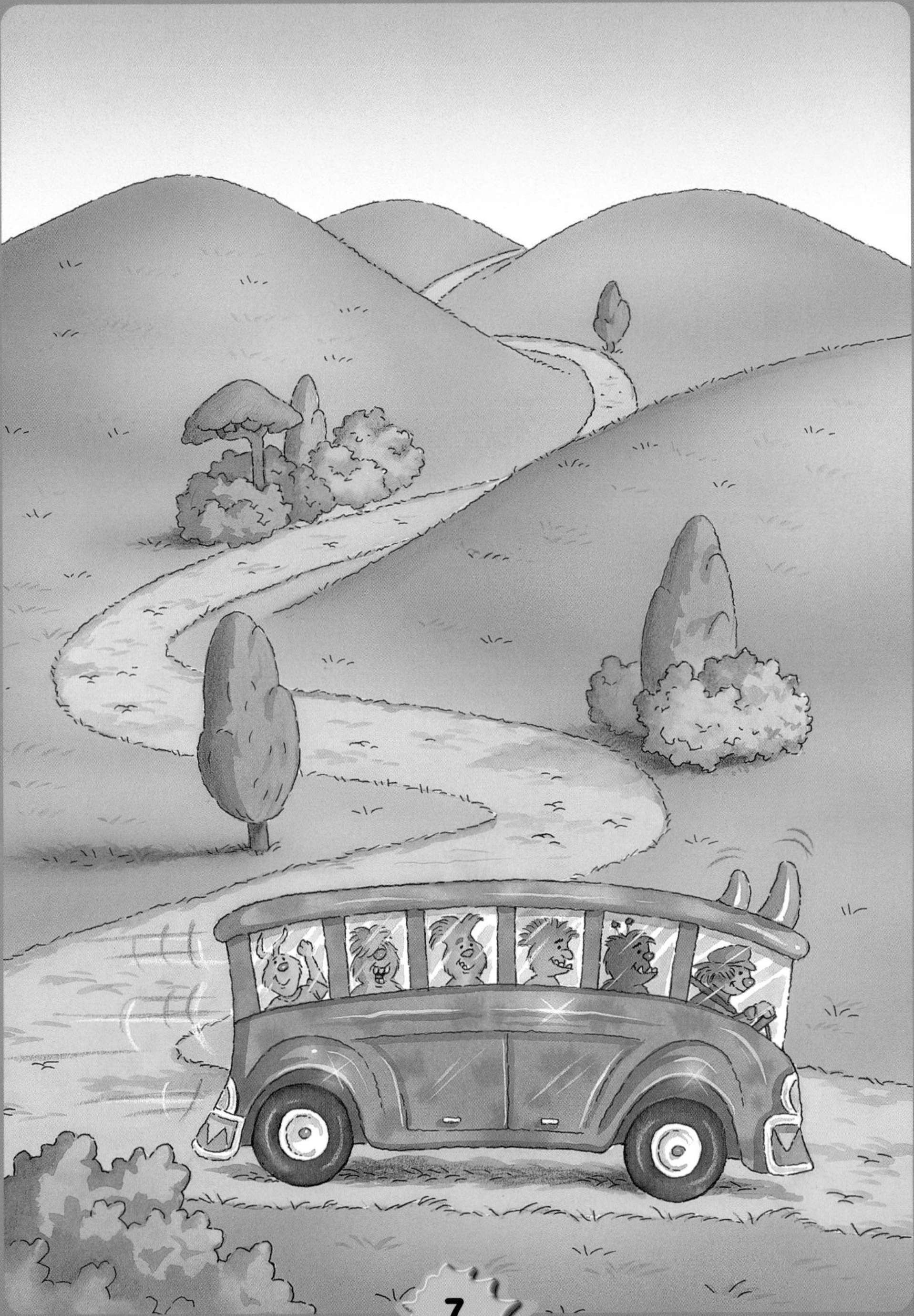

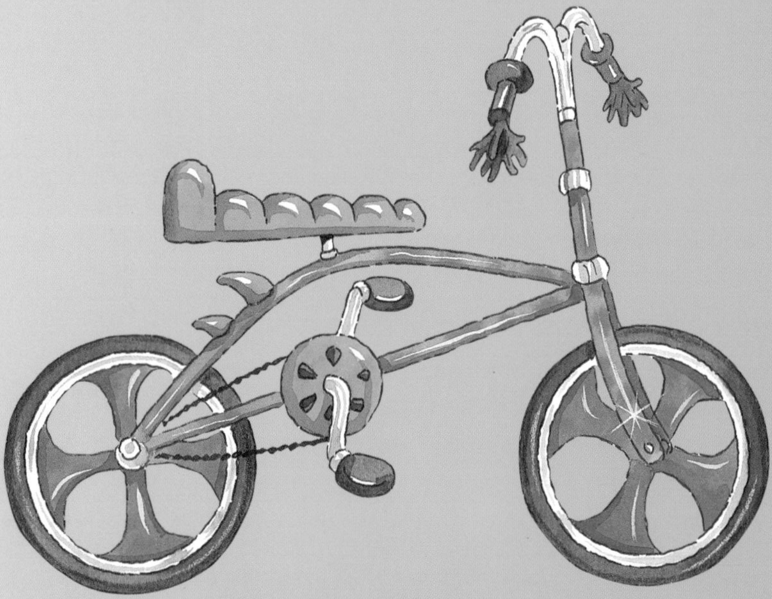

A bike.

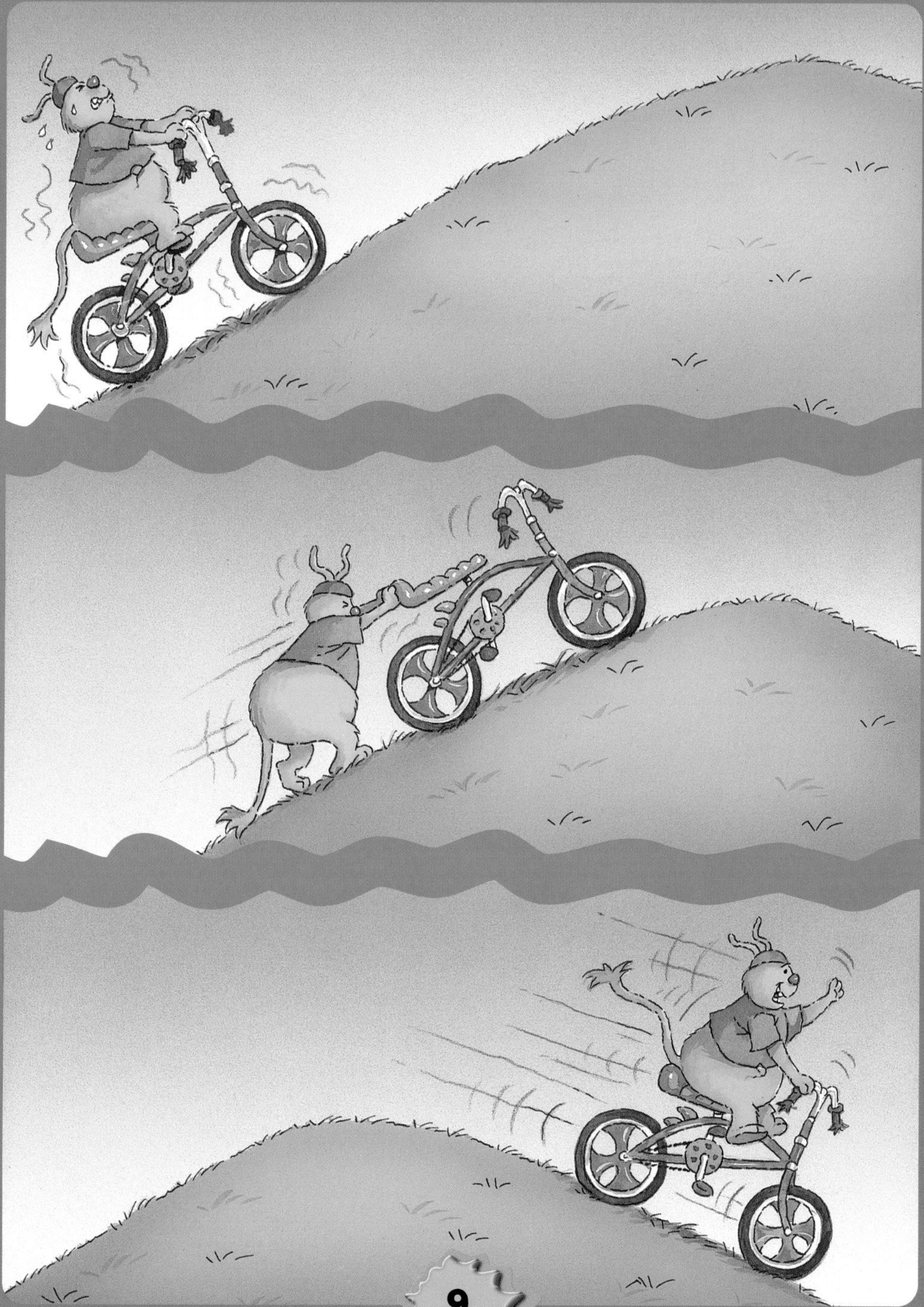

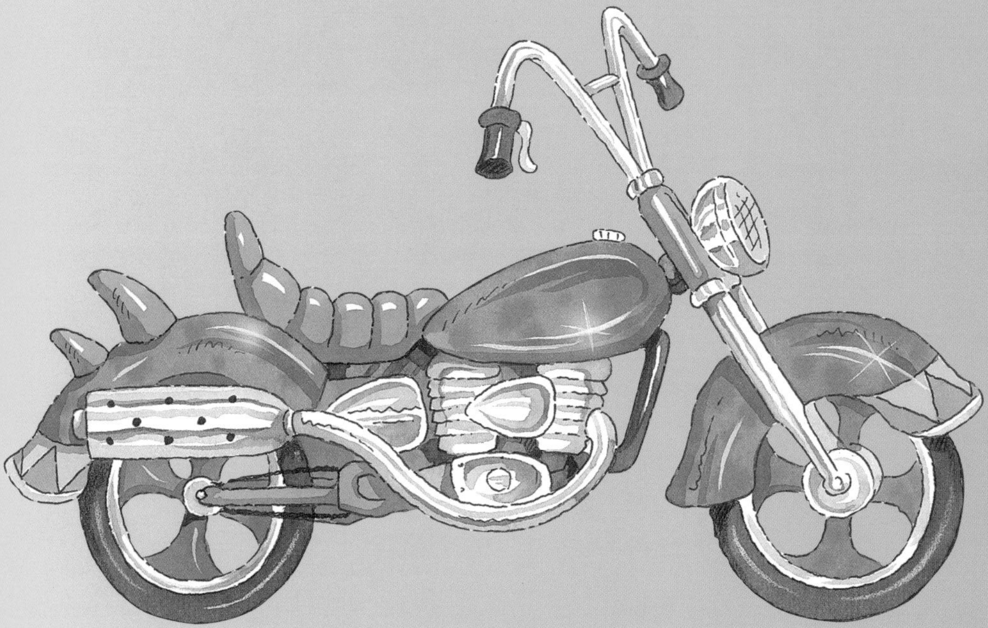

A motorbike.

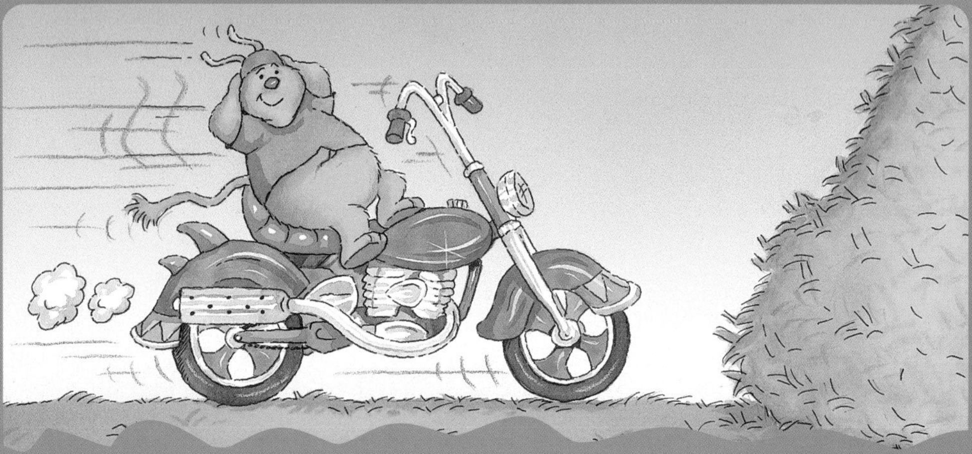

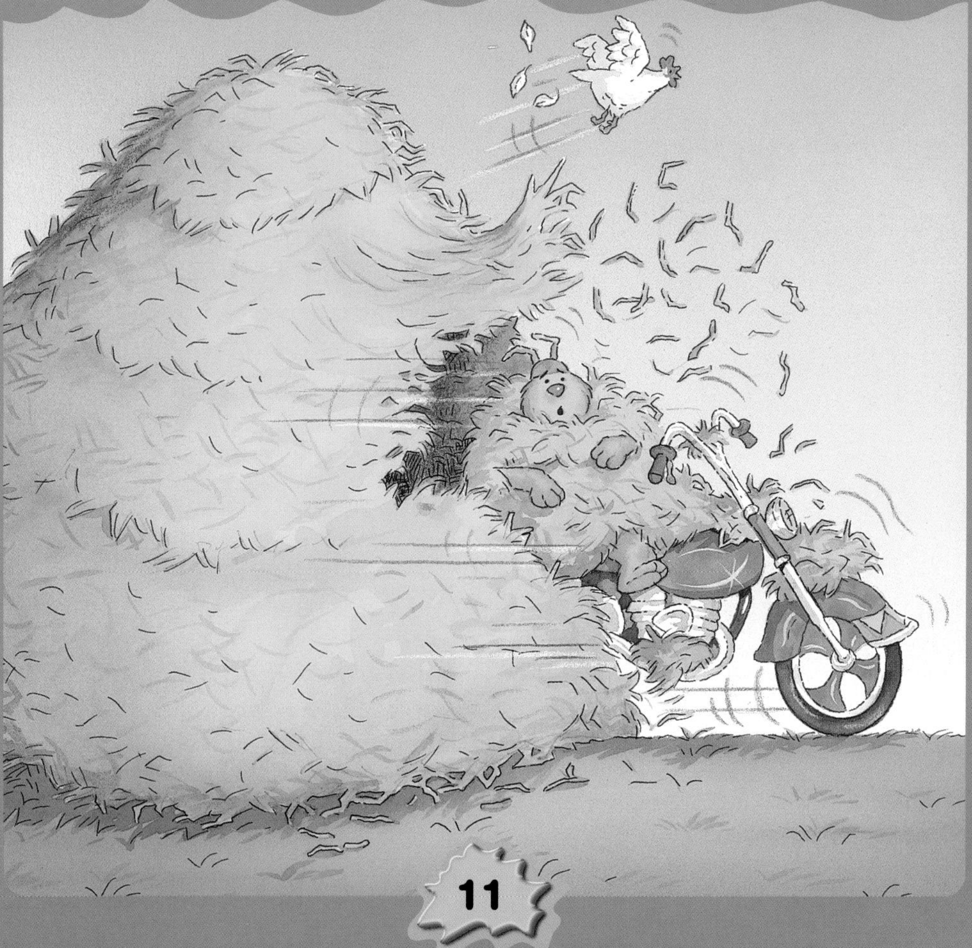

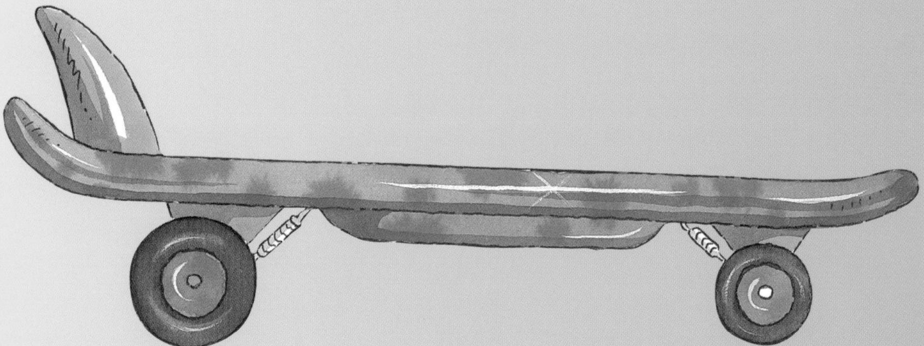

A skateboard.

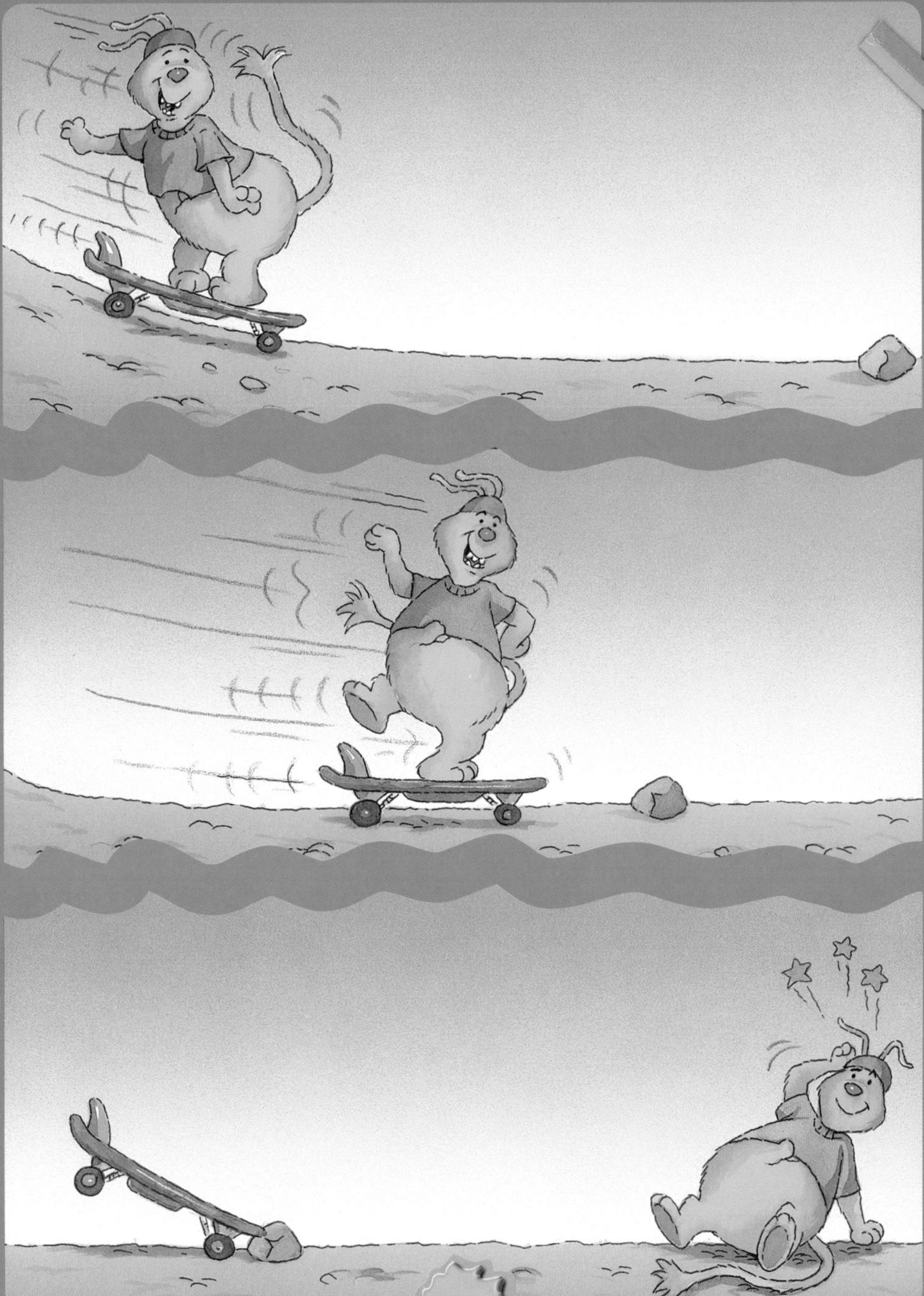

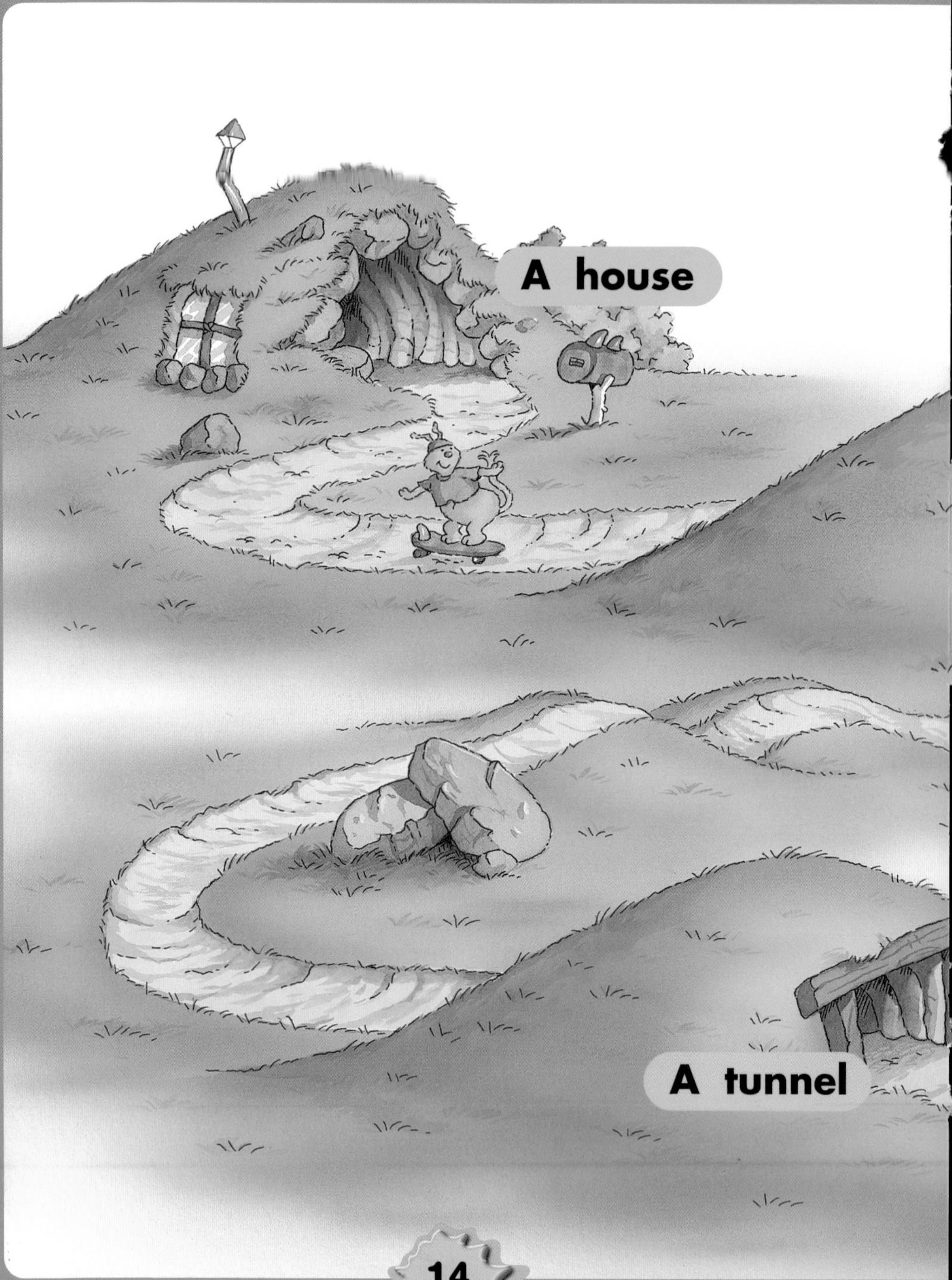
A house
A tunnel

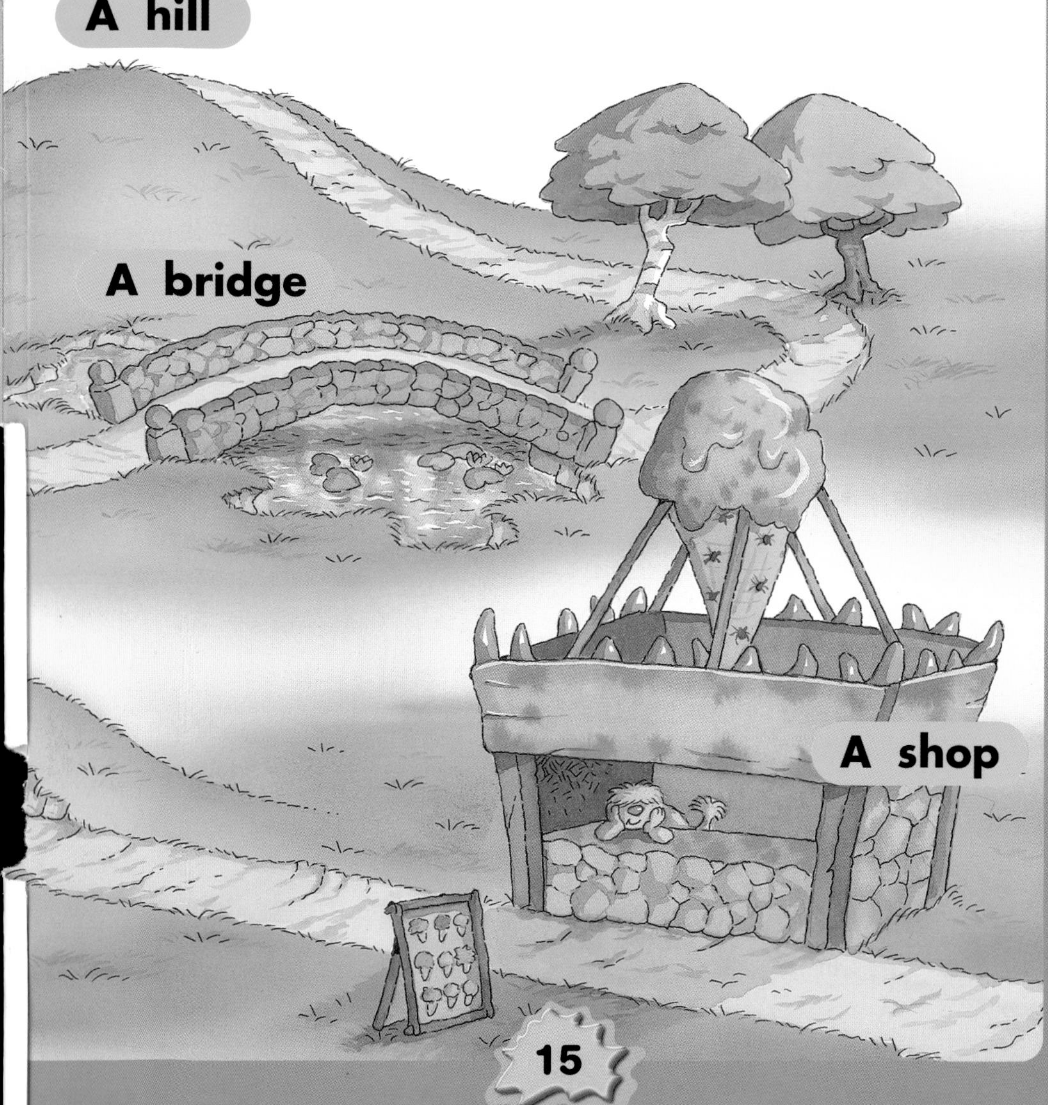
A hill
A bridge
A shop

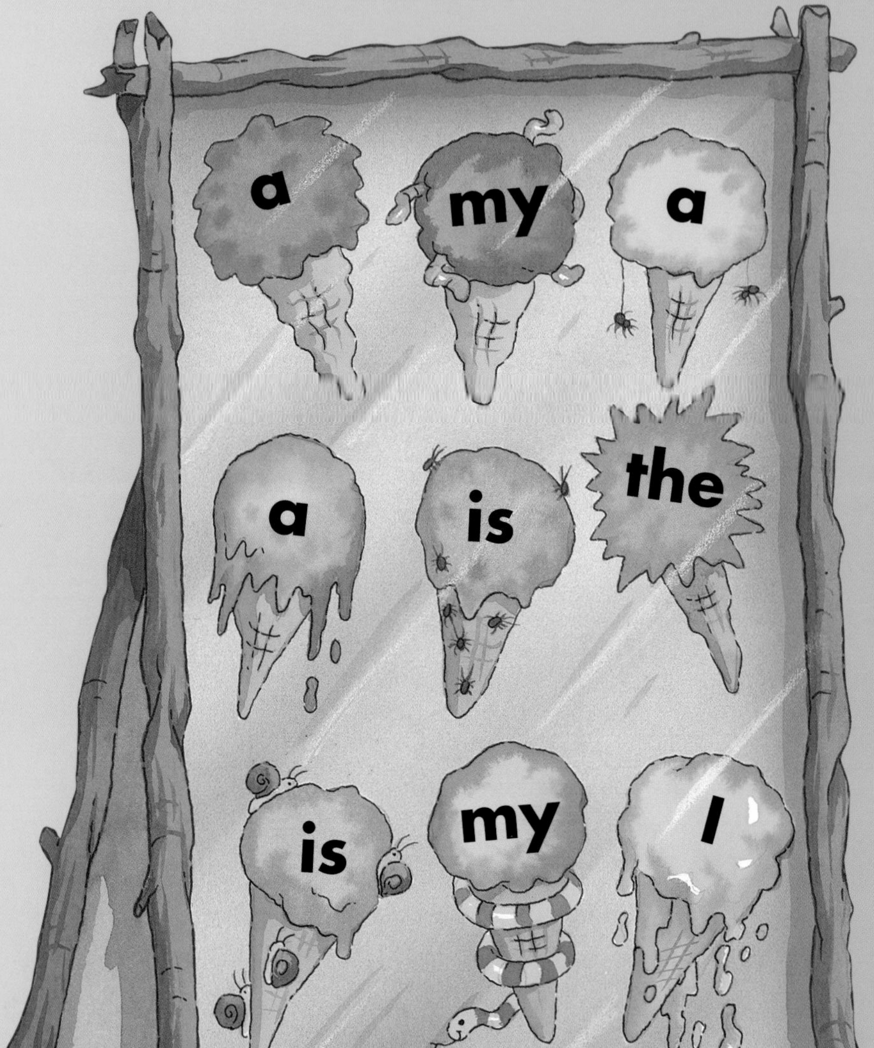
a
my
a
a
is
the
is
my
I